P

MW00778545

Abortion-Related Stress in Psychiatric Outpatients

Comparisons among Abortion-Distressed, Abortion-Non-Distressed, and No-Abortion Groups

David C. Hanley, Rachel L. Anderson, David B. Larson, Harry L. Piersma, D. Stephen King, Roger C. Sider

En Route Books & Media, LLC
St. Louis, MO

En Route Books and Media, LLC
5705 Rhodes Avenue
St. Louis, MO 63109

Library of Congress Control Number: 2020937394

ISBN-13: 978-1-952464-08-9

David C. Hanley, Harry L. Piersma, D. Stephen King, and Roger C. Sider at
Pine Rest Christian Hospital, Grand Rapids, Michigan; **Rachel L. Anderson at
Department of Human Development and Social Policy, Northwestern
University, Evanston, Illinois; David B. Larson at National Institute for Health
Care Research, Washington DC, and Department of Psychiatry, Northwestern
University Medical School, Chicago, Illinois.

This research was supported by the Pine Rest Foundation. Presented at the
American Psychological Association's annual conference, New York, 1995.

ABSTRACT

Objective: This study examines potential risk factors for long-term abortion-related distress in women.

Method: One hundred and two women receiving outpatient psychiatric services were assigned to one of three groups on the basis of their reported abortion history. Women with a positive history of abortion were assigned to a distressed or non-distressed group depending on whether abortion-related distress was a primary presenting problem. Women with no history of abortion who sought outpatient services served as controls.

Results: Comparisons across groups revealed that the abortion-distressed group had symptoms consistent with Posttraumatic Stress Disorder, including intrusive thoughts of the abortion experience and active avoidance of events associated with their abortions. Two women who underwent an abortion following rape were both in the abortion-distressed group.

Conclusions: Implications for identifying women at risk for long-term distress are discussed and suggestions for clinical interventions are made.

Key Words: Abortion, Posttraumatic Stress Disorder, Women's Health

CONTENTS

THE ARGUMENT

The United States Supreme Court decision of Roe v. Wade in 1973 legalized the practice of elective abortion. This decision stimulated a period of considerable research examining psychological effects arising from the use of elective abortion techniques to terminate pregnancies. Studies have examined the prevalence of negative sequelae of abortion such as guilt, depression, and suicide (Adler, 1975; Cohen & Roth, 1984; Franco, Tamburrino, Pentz & Jurs, 1989). These studies have surveyed women one week to ten years after their most recent abortion, with most studies covering a year or less of the post-abortion period (Lyons, Larson, Huckeba, Rogers & Mueller, 1988).

More recent reviews indicate a relatively small minority of women undergoing elective abortions who report significant psychological reactions (Dagg, 1991; Adler, David, Major, Roth, Russo &

Wyatt, 1992). A primary risk factor predictive of negative reaction was a prior history of psychiatric disorders. A recent review by Anderson, Lyons, and Larson (1994) reports little use in the peer-reviewed research of careful diagnostic criteria to specify the prevalence of psychiatric conditions that might be associated with or attributable to the experience of undergoing a previous elective abortion. This observation is consistent with Dagg (1991) that the research on psychological reactions to abortion suffered the following methodological limitations— a lack of conceptual models to explain adjustment reactions, a lack of reliable diagnostic measures, an absence of appropriate comparison groups.

Available literature does indicate that rates of abortion-related distress occur with sufficient frequency to merit scientific investigation. Ney, Fung, Wickett and Beaman-Dodd (1994) estimate that 25% of women who have had pregnancy losses feel they need professional help. These authors report that women who abort electively appear to require more and more sophisticated grief counseling than those who suffer other types of pregnancy loss (e.g., stillbirth, miscarriage). Further data reported by the American Psychological

Association (1987) suggest that distress prevalence ranges from 0.5% to 1.5%. As the number of abortions performed in the United States rises, the number of affected women is likely to increase proportionally. While most women who undergo abortions do not have negative psychological reactions, these data suggest that some women do experience negative psychological and psychiatric sequelae secondary to the abortion experience. It is the experience of these women that the present study addresses.

The relatively low levels of physical and psychological risk associated with elective abortion found in the literature (Anderson, Lyons, & Larson, 1994) suggests that factors apart from the procedure per se may be responsible for post-abortion stress. It appears that certain factors, such as previous psychiatric difficulties, put women at greater risk for poor psychological adjustment (Dagg, 1991). If prior psychological difficulties precurse negative reactions to abortion, then it would be reasonable to propose that psychological processes mediate women's response. This suggests that the process of coping with the abortion experience may vary across women.

At least three psychological models appear relevant to the consideration of women's psychological reactions: posttraumatic stress, stress and coping (adjustment disorders), and existential/moral guilt.

The Posttraumatic Stress Disorder (PTSD) model posits a diagnosable psychiatric disorder which results from a traumatic experience. In order to explain reactions to abortion within this model, DSM-IV criteria require that the experience of the abortion would have to be traumatic for the affected women and that their symptoms following the abortion would have to be consistent with the symptom profile of PTSD and include persistent re-experiencing of the abortion, persistent avoidance of stimuli associated with the abortion, and persistent symptoms of increased arousal (American Psychological Association, 1994).

Several sub-clinical alternatives to the PTSD model exist that might be applicable to understanding adverse psychological reactions to abortion. For example, the 'stress and coping' model would posit that abortion is an intervention of varying levels of stress to women and that a woman's coping style and resiliency would predict response to the experience. Positive adaptation to an abortion is influenced by a complex interplay of life events including marital status (Adler, 1975; Payne, Dravitz & Notman, 1976), coercion by significant others to abort (Waters, 1980), insufficient social and psychosocial instability (Adler & Dolcini, 1986; Major, 1994; Robbins & DeLamater, 1985), and co-occurring stress due to other major life events (Blumberg, Golbus & Hanson, 1975; Moseley, Follingstad, Harley & Heckel, 1981). Few emotional problems would result if a woman either did not experience the abortion as stressful or she had sufficient coping skills and resources. On the other hand, if a woman experienced the abortion as stressful and had poor coping abilities and limited social supports, she could be at risk for adverse psychological outcome.

Alternatively, the 'existential/moral' model of adjustment to abortion would understand psychological responses in terms of the meaning of the abortion to the woman undergoing the procedure. In a situation where the woman was comfortable with her decision and did not experience her choice as personally unacceptable, this model would predict healthy psychological adjustment. On the other hand, if her abortion choice conflicted with her moral beliefs and/or values, or if the abortion had meaning (e.g., conceived from a recently failed marriage), then the woman would be at risk for poor psychological adjustment to the extent that she could not resolve her choice of an abortion relative to her values and beliefs.

Issues of morality and spirituality associated with decisions about abortion, although salient in personal and public concerns, have been infrequently addressed in scientific studies. Studies which assess the role of religious beliefs and commitment on women's response to abortion are scarce. Further, when religiousness has been measured in scientific literature, it has been most often reported as a religious or denominational affiliation variable without in-depth analysis (Larson, Pattison, Blazer, Omran, & Kaplan, 1986). Failure to adequately address religious commitment and beliefs could produce results that do not accurately or fully reflect psychological reactions in studies of abortion related psychological distress.

The present study proposes to test whether or not women who report distress from their abortion experience fit a profile with PTSD or whether an alternative model of psychological adjustment is warranted. In order to address the primary methodological concerns of this literature, a reliable diagnostic interview for PTSD will be used along with multiple comparison groups. Specifically, the symptom profiles of PTSD are compared between women with psychiatric disorders who report distress associated with a prior abortion relative to women with psychiatric disorders who report no adjustment problems associated with a prior abortion and women with psychiatric problems who have no reported history of a prior abortion.

METHOD

Subjects

One hundred and two participants were drawn from a population of women receiving outpatient psychiatric services between March 1990 and July 1991. One hundred women in the abortion-distressed group were White, one woman was Black, and one woman was Latino. All participants were at least 18 years old. Eighty-two women were recruited from current cases of the outpatient psychiatric facility of a hospital. An additional twenty women whose presenting psychiatric problems involved their psychological adjustment to a previous elective abortion were recruited via mail solicitations to therapists in the community.

All women were screen for psychosis by a psychiatrist. No women were excluded from the study based on this criterion. Participants were assigned to one of three experimental groups based upon their reported abortion-related experiences.

Comparison Groups

Three groups were formed for the present study. One group consisted of women who sought psychiatric services in response to their psychological adjustment to an abortion. The group will be referred to as the abortion-distressed group (A-D). The first comparison group consisted of women who reported having a prior abortion but did not present for psychiatric services because of any psychological problems experienced from that event. The group will be referred to as the abortion-non-distressed group (A-ND). The second comparison group consisted of women who sought psychiatric services but who reported no history of an elective abortion. This group will be referred to as the no-abortion group (N-A).

The A-D group consisted of 26 women (mean age 30.3) whose primary presenting problem for outpatient services was distress related to a prior elective abortion.

The A-ND group consisted of 22 women (mean age 32.5) who reported at least one prior elective abortion, but whose presenting problems for outpatient services were not abortion related.

The N-A group consisted of 54 women (mean age 36.8) seeking outpatient services with no prior history of elective abortion.

The Posttraumatic Stress Disorder (PTSD) module of the Structured Clinical Interview for DSM-III-R (SCID-R) (Spitzer, Williams & Gibbon, 1987) was utilized. This instrument is a structured interview which assesses the 17 PTSD symptoms from the DSM-III-R across the criteria categories of re-experiencing, numbing-avoidance, and physiological arousal. In all cases, the SCID-R, for both current and lifetime PTSD, was administered by a board-certified psychiatrist. For each participant, the score on the PTSD module was zero through three according to the number of criterion categories that were positive.

The Interview for Recent Life Events (IRLE) is a semi-structured interview used to assess the number and severity of stressful life events during the previous six-month period (Paykel, 1974). Nine areas of stressful events are measured: work, education, finance, health, bereavement, migration, courtship, family and social relationships, and marital relationship. For this study, additional questions were added to the IRLE. Participants were asked if they ever had an elective abortion. Additionally, participants were asked to indicate the most stressful life event they had ever experienced, and the most stressful life event they had experienced in the previous six months. These later two questions were asked at the end of the interview in order to minimize any effects of asking about the abortion experience.

The Minnesota Multiphasic Personality Inventory-2 (MMPI-2) is a widely used self-report inventory designed to assess major patterns of personality and emotional disorders (Butcher, Dahlstrom, Graham, Telegan & Kremmer, 1989). This instrument consists of 567 true/false items forming seven validity indicators and ten clinical scales. The MMPI-2 was used to control concurrent psychiatric distress by examining clinically significant psychopathology across experimental groups.

There are two subscales of the MMPI-2 which specifically assess posttraumatic stress disorder. The MMPI-2 PK scale was developed by Keane, Malloy, and Fairbank (1984) to differentiate Veterans Administration psychiatric patients who were diag-nosed as experiencing posttraumatic stress disorder from those who did not. The MMPI-2 PS scale was developed through the work of Schlenger and Kulka (1987). Whereas the PK scale was developed and validated by a psychiatric population, the PS scale by contrast was developed by determining which items discriminated Vietnam era veterans who manifested posttraumatic symptoms without associated psycho-pathology.

The Los Angeles Symptom Checklist is a 43-item self-report inventory assessing psychological distress across a variety of psychosocial domains (e.g., de-pression, anxiety, drinking, relationship problems, difficulty concentrating) as they relate to PTSD. Each item is rated on a 5-point scale from 0, not a problem to 4, an extreme problem. Severity ratings for all 43 items were summed up to form the Total Score, a continuous measure of global psychological distress (a possible range of 0 to 172). The LASC has been used with a variety of community and clinical popu-lations including veterans, battered women, adult survivors of sexual abuse, and adolescent victims of community violence. The LASC has been shown to have high internal consistency (.95), test, re-test reliability, and satisfactory concurrent validity (Sarason, Levine, Bashaam & Sarason, 1983).

The Social Support Questionnaire-6 (Sarason, Sarason, Shearin & Pierce, 1987) is a six-item shortened version of the Social Support Questionnaire (Sarason et al., 1983). This tool is a self-report inventory assessing the number of persons within one's network perceived to be potential sources of social support and one's satisfaction with the quality and extent of that social support.

The Impact of Event Scale (IES) (Horowitz, Wilner & Alvarez, 1979) is a 15-item scale which was designed to measure an individual's response to a specific stressor. Respondents were asked to rate their most stressful life experience. Two major response tendencies are assessed: intrusion (re-experiencing) of the stressful event and avoidance (denial) of the stressful event. Research has suggested that individuals who meet criteria for PTSD have higher intrusion and avoidance scale scores than those who do not (Weisenberg, Solomon, Schwarzwald & Mikulincer, 1987).

Finally, the Abortion-Related Psychosocial History Interview (ARPHI) is a semi-structured clinical interview designed for use in the present study to gather information concerning the abortion experience (number of abortions, method of abortion, medical complications). The ARPHI is based in part on Speckhard's (1987) abortion stress interview and measures the psychosocial context at the time of the abortion (e.g., marital and socioeconomic status, partner and parent involvement and support, religious involvement, preexisting and concurrent psychiatric history, personal beliefs regarding the morality of abortion, etc.). The ARPHI was administered in interview format by a board-certified social worker.

Procedure

Prior to assessment, informed consent was obtained. All participants completed the MMPI-2 and LASC. Each participant was then assessed and administered the SCID-R and the IRLE. All participants subsequently completed the SSQ-6 and the IES. All women who reported having received an elective abortion were administered the ARPHI.

Statistical Analysis

For measures given to all subjects, groups were compared using one-way ANOVA's followed by post hoc comparisons of means (Tukey HSD) when the F statistic was significant ($p < .05$). Given that a number of comparisons were made across measures, a Bonferroni correction (within domain of variables) was used to establish a $p < .01$ criteria for statistical significance.

RESULT

Demographics

The groups were compared on a variety of demographic variables. Results indicate no significant differences among groups at the time of the interview in mean level of education, employment status, financial independence, number living with family members, or religious affiliation. A significant effect was found for age at interview. Women in the N-A (mean of 36.8 years) group were significantly older than the women in A-D (mean of 30.3 years) group

(F $(2,101)$ = 8.02, p< .001). There were no differences in age between the N-A and A-ND (mean 32.5 years) groups or between A-D and A-ND groups. Additionally, women in the A-D group (61 % single) were, at the time of the interview, significantly more likely to be single than the women in the A-ND (17% single) and N-A (22% single) groups who were more likely to be married (X^2 = 15.4, df = 2, p<.001).

Significantly less time had passed between the abortion and the interview for the A-D women (7.7 years) than the A-ND women (12.1 years) (t = 2.63, df = 46, p< .01). No differences between the A-D and A-ND groups were found regarding woman's age at abortion, partner's age at abortion, the use of birth control, or length of time with partner at the time of abortion. No differences between groups were found for number of prior abortions. Twenty-one percent of the A-D women and 26% of the A-ND women had a reported history of multiple abortions.

Finally, women were asked whether they had experienced a prior history of child physical and/or sexual abuse, incest, rape, or domestic violence (specifically being a battered partner). While both abortion groups reported high levels of prior physical and sexual abuse, there were no significant differences between groups (overall 68% of the A-D group as compared to 72% of the A-ND group). Specifically, 11% of the A-D women reported experiencing childhood physical abuse, 7% experienced childhood sexual abuse, 36% experienced incest, 32% experienced rape, and 36% reported they had been battered by a partner.

Comparatively, 21% of women in the A-ND group reported experiencing childhood physical abuse, 11% experienced childhood sexual abuse, 26% experienced incest, 11% experienced rape, and 32% reported they had been battered.

Posttraumatic Stress Disorder

Using the SCID-R diagnostic scheme, the Impact of Events Scale, the MMPI-2 subscales, and the LASC, groups were compared on PTSD. For the SCID-R, the A-D women had significantly more diagnostic signs of PTSD than did the A-ND and the N-A women ($X^2 = 35.6$, df = 2, p< .00001). Nineteen of the 26 women (73.1%) in the A-D group met all four of the diagnostic criteria for PTSD according to the SCID-R; experiencing the event as traumatic, persistent re-experiencing of the event, avoidance, and arousal. This compared to 9.1% of the women in the A-ND group and 13.5% of the women in the N-A group.

Twenty-five of the 26 A-D women completed the SCID-R relative to their abortion experience. One woman completed the SCID-R relative to her father's death. This latter woman did not meet the diagnostic criteria for PTSD.

For 20 of the 26 women in the A-D group, their abortion represented the most stressful experience in their life. This compared to only three women for whom their abortion was the most stressful life experience in the A-ND group.

Results measuring differences on the Impact of Events Scale was consistent with the pattern observed with the SCID-R. The A-D women had much higher levels of intrusive thoughts ($F_{(2,99)}$ = 16.57, $p < .001$) and avoidance ($F_{(2,99)}$ = 8.5, $p < .001$) than the two comparison groups. For intrusive thoughts, all three groups were significantly different with the A-D women experiencing the highest levels of intrusive thoughts, followed by the A-ND women and finally the N-A group. For thoughts of avoidance, the A-D group experienced significantly higher levels of avoidance than the other two groups.

One of the three Los Angeles Symptom Checklist scales was significantly different across groups. The A-D group had higher levels of persistent re-experiencing of the trauma as compared to both the A-ND and N-A groups ($F_{(2,99)}$ = 9.78, $p < .0001$).

There were no differences among groups on the LASC for avoidance associated with the trauma or persistent increased arousal.

Finally, no significant group differences were found on the MMPI-2 measuring general psychiatric symptomatology or on the PTSD-related MMPI-PK and MMPI-PS subscales.

Table 1 on page 31 summarizes these results.

Social Support and Life Events

There were no differences between groups in their level of perceived social support as measured by the SSQ-6. There were significant differences between groups as measured by the IRLE. The A-ND reported more adverse life events than either of the other groups (F (2,99) = 5.53, p< .005). No differences were found between the A-D and N-A groups.

Abortion Reason/Experience

While seven women in the study reported having been raped, two of the women sought an abortion following a rape-induced pregnancy. Both of these women were in the A-D group. There were no differences between groups regarding the period of time between pregnancy testing and the abortion procedure, week of pregnancy at time of abortion, the receipt of abortion counseling, procedure type, or complications and hospitalizations due to the abortion experience. Further, there were no differences between groups regarding the term used to describe what was aborted. However, approximately 75% of both groups described that which was aborted as a 'baby'. There were no differences between groups on church/temple attendance, importance of religion, or relationship with God, pastor/rabbi, or church members at time of interview. However, the A-D group (43%) as compared to the A-ND group (5%) more often expressed the belief that abortion was morally wrong (p< .003). Finally, there was a trend that the A-D group was less likely as compared to the A-ND group to have been driven home from the abortion by a friend or family member ($X^2 = 7.41$, df = 2, p< .02).

DISCUSSION

In the present study, structured clinician-rated diagnostic assessments revealed a higher rate of PTSD in women seeking outpatient psychiatric services for problems associated with a prior abortion experience as compared to women with a history of abortion who were seeking outpatient services for other problems. The high rate of PTSD among these women is in contrast to the minimal differences among groups on measures of overall social support and measures of religiosity. Additionally, the abortion-distressed group was not different from other women seeking mental health services in terms of pathology as measured by the MMPI-2. Further, abortion-distressed women experienced fewer recent adverse life events as compared to the abortion-non-distressed women seeking mental health services for other reasons. Thus, higher levels of PTSD experienced in the A-D women cannot be explained by these potential confounds.

The abortion experience was traumatic for the abortion-distressed women as they reported experiencing significantly higher levels of intrusive thoughts and active avoidance, as measured in the Impact of Event Scale, even years after the procedure. Related to these findings is the notion that the adaptions occur in response to the core symptoms of PTSD rather than specifically to the traumatic event (Southwick, Yehuda & Giller, 1993). Adapting to and living with symptoms of psychiatric illness can lead to changes in an individual's coping style. For example, women in the A-D group reported experiencing higher levels of sleep disturbance than women in the A-ND group.

Historical differences among groups might also explain the observed differences in rates of PTSD. Fierman et al. (1993) suggest that sexual assault at any age, as well as childhood physical abuse, may account for a significantly higher rate of PTSD in individuals reporting these types of trauma. The present findings are not consistent with this explanation. While the A-D and A-ND groups both experienced high rates of prior physical and sexual abuse

(68% compared to 72% respectively), rates did not statistically differ between groups. It may be note-worthy, however, that the two women who received elective abortions after rape-induced pregnancy both had abortion-related PTSD. Thus, although overall histories of sexual trauma did not differentiate groups, abortions that terminate rape-induced preg-nancies might be particularly traumatic.

While the association of prior objective events did not explain higher levels of PTSD, the subjective meaning of any event may (Perry, Difede, Musngi, Frances & Jacobsberg, 1992). In fact, DSM-IV has increased the flexibility in the diagnosis of PTSD from requiring an objective determination of the 'traumatic' nature of the event to also include the subjective experience of the event from the patient's perspective. Thus, understanding PTSD involves an assessment of the affected person's experience of trauma. For present purposes, this means that difference in the development of PTSD across groups of women might be explained, in part, through differences in the subjective experience of the abor-tion. Several investigators have suggested that pretrauma personality is linked to the development of PTSD. Specifically, that preexisting emotional problems or disorders may render an individual susceptible to the development of a posttraumatic syndrome (Southwick, Yehuda & Giller, 1993).

Examining subjective factors associated with the abortion experience as the trauma event, two findings are notable. First, there were no differences between the A-D group and the A-ND group for the term used to describe what was aborted. Approximately 75% of the time, both groups referred to that which was aborted as a 'baby'. However, the two groups did significantly differ in their belief that abortion was morally wrong. Specifically, for some women the abortion may have violated their moral code. Such an experience of a moral transgression appears to be related to a greater susceptibility to PTSD. Consistent with this, Southwick, Yehuda & Giller (1993) suggest that even when individuals are not the direct recipient of a threat, they can experience distress. However, the present study is a retrospective analysis evaluating psychiatric symptoms years after the abortion experience. Such an analysis precludes determining whether the development of PTSD is related to the individual's emotional state at the time of the abortion. Prospective follow-along designs that sample broadly and assess both the women's experience of the abortion and her long-term adjustment are needed to understand factors that may place some women at risk for PTSD.

A second limitation to the present study, the SCID PTSD module was utilized alone; the entire SCID was not given to participants. As Southwick et al. (1993) report, high rates of co-morbid psychopathology have been associated with PTSD including major depression and substance abuse. However, the presence of co-morbid psychopathology does not rule out the existence of PTSD. Future research should examine the effects of co-occurring disorders to better understand potential distress experienced by some women who undergo abortion procedures. A more extensive understanding of PTSD and co-occurring disorders would provide clinicians with a more comprehensive understanding of women with abortion experiences seeking psychiatric services. Such understanding would aid in the development of more effective treatment for these women.

An additional methodological consideration results from the finding that A-D women had experienced an elective abortion more recently than the A-ND women. This suggests that time may reduce some of the adverse psychological reaction to the abortion. However, for the A-D women, the average time from abortion was nearly eight years.

A final methodological consideration involves the sampling used in the present study. It is important to note that while the findings indicate that PTSD can result from a prior elective abortion, there is no evidence from the present data on how frequently such a reaction might be observed. The present sample was recruited to specifically over-sample women who were experiencing difficulties adjusting to their abortion experience.

In sum, the present results suggest that some women experience PTSD as a result of elective abortion. It appears that this experience is not mediated by social support, history of abuse, other psychopathology, or life events. It does appear that the occurrence of PTSD might be related to a woman's experience of the abortion as outside her normal values or morality. These findings, if replicated, have potentially important prevention and treatment implications for persons working with women who are considering an abortion, are under-going an abortion, or are living with the past experience of an elective abortion. Prevention of PTSD might occur through intervention prior to or during the abortion. Treatment of adverse reaction to abortion might benefit from considering the research on interventions with PTSD resulting from other traumatic events.

TABLE 1

Comparison of means on PTSD-related measures among Abortion-Distressed (A-D), Abortion-Non-Distressed (A-ND) and No Abortion (N-A) women seeking outpatient mental health services

Variable	A-D	A-ND	N-A	Significance Level
SCID-R*	73.1%	9.1%	13.5%	p< .00001
LASC re-experiencing	6.8	3.0	3.7	p< .0001
LASC avoidance	12.7	9.6	10.7	NS
LASC arousal	10.2	8.7	10.0	NS
MMPI-PK	71.6	64.2	67.3	NS
MMPI-PS	68.7	68.2	64.4	NS
IES intrusion	12.1	3.2	8.6	p< .0001
IES avoidance	13.2	5.8	8.5	p< .0005

*Percent of women meeting all four of the diagnostic criteria for PTSD according to the SCID-R; experiencing the event as traumatic, persistent re-experiencing of the event, avoidance, and arousal.

REFERENCES

Adler, N.E. (1975). Emotional responses of women following therapeutic abortion. *American Journal of Orthopsychiatry*, 45, 446–454.

Adler, N.E., David, H.P., Major, B.D., Roth, S.H., Russo, N.G, Wyatt, G.E. (1992). Psychological factors in abortion: A review. *American Psychologist*, 47, 1194–1204.

Adler, N.E., Dolcini, P. (1986). Psychological issues in abortion for adolescents, in G.B. Melton (ed.) *Adolescent abortion: Psychological and legal issues*. Lincoln, NE: University of Nebraska Press.

American Psychological Association. (1994). *Diagnostic and Statistical Manual of Mental Disorders,* Fourth edition, Washington, D.C.

American Psychological Association. (1987). Research review presented to the Office of the Surgeon General of the United States.

Anderson, R.L., Lyons, J.S., Larson, D.B. (1994). A systematic review of the physical, psychological and social impact of induced abortion on women. Paper presented at the American Psychological Association's conference on women's health, Washington, D.C.

Blumberg, B.D., Golbus, M.S., Hanson, K.H. (1975). The psychological sequelae of abortion performed for a genetic indication. *American Journal of Obstetrics and Gynecology*, 122:7, 799–808.

Butcher, J.N., Dahlstrom, W.G., Graham, J.R., Telegan, A., Kremmer, B. (1989). *Manual for the restandardized Minnesota Multiphasic Personality Inventory: MMPI-2. An interpretive and administrative guide.* Minneapolis: University of Minnesota Press.

Cohen, T., Roth, S. (1984). Coping with abortion. *Journal of Human Stress*, 10, 140–145.

Dagg, P.K.B. (1991). The psychological sequelae of therapeutic abortion. *American Journal of Psychiatry* 148, 578–585.

Fierman, E.J., Hunt, M.F., Pratt, L.A., Warshaw, M.G., Yonkers, K.A, Peterson, L.G., Epstein-Kaye, T.M., Norton, H.S. (1993). Trauma and posttraumatic stress disorder in subjects with anxiety disorders. *American Journal of Psychiatry*, 150:12, 1872–1874.

Franco, K.N., Tamburrino, M.B., Campbell, N.B., Pentz, P.E., Jurs, S.G. (1989). Psychological profile of dysphoric women postabortion. *JAMWA*, 44:4, 113–115.

Horowitz, M., Wilner, H. Alvarez, W. (1979). Impact of Events Scale: A measure of subjective stress. *Psychosomatic Medicine*, 41, 209–218.

Keane, T.M., Malloy, P.F., Fairbank, J.A. (1984). Empirical development of an MMPI subscale for the assessment of combat-related posttraumatic stress disorder. *Journal of Consulting and Clinical Psychology*, 52, 888–891.

Larson, D.B., Pattison, E.M., Blazer, D.G., Omran, A.R., Kaplan, B.H. (1986) Systematic analysis of research on religious variables in four major psychiatric journals, 1978–1982. *American Journal of Psychiatry*, 143:3, 329–334.

Lyons, J.S., Larson, D.B., Huckeba, W.M., Rogers, J.L. Mueller, C.P. (1988). Research on the psychosocial impact of abortion: A systematic review of the literature 1966 to 1985. In *Values &*

Public Policy, Gerald P. Regier (ed.). Washington, D.C.: Family Research Council of America, Inc.

Major, B. (1994). Social conflict, social support, and adjustment to abortion. Paper presented at the American Psychological Association's conference on women's health, Washington, D.C.

Moseley, O.T., Follingstad, D.R., Harley, H., Heckel, R. (1981). Psychological factors that predict reaction to abortion. *Journal of Clinical Psychology*, 37, 276–279.

Ney, P.G., Fung, T., Wickett, A.R., Beaman-Dodd, C. (1994). The effects of pregnancy loss on women's health. *Social Science Medicine*, 38:9, 1193–1200.

Paykel, E.S. (1974). Life stress and psychiatric disorder: Application of the clinical approach. In B.P. Dohrenwend & B.S. Dohrenwend (eds.) *Stressful life events: their nature and effects* (pp. 135–149). New York: Wiley.

Payne, E., Kravitz, A., Notman, M. (1976). Outcome following therapeutic abortion. *Archives of General Psychiatry*, 33, 725–733.

Perry, S., Difede, J., Musngi, G., Frances, A.J., Jacobsberg, L. (1992). Predictors of posttraumatic stress disorder after burn injury. *American Journal of Psychiatry*, 149:7, 931–935.

Robbins, J.M., DeLamater, J.D. (1985). Support from significant others and loneliness following induced abortion. *Social Psychiatry*, 20, 92–99.

Sarason, I.G.. Levine, H.M., Bashaam, R.B. (1983). Assessing social support: The Social Support Questionnaire. *Journal of Personality and Social Psychology*, 44, 127–139.

Sarason, I.G., Sarason, B.R., Shearin, E.N., Pierce, G.R. (1987). A brief measure of social support: Practical and theoretical limitations. *Journal of Social and Personal Relationships*, 4, 497–510.

Schlenger, W.E., Kulka, R.A. (1987). Performance of the Keane-Fairbank MMPI Scale and other self-report measures in identifying posttraumatic stress disorder. Paper presented at the American Psychological Association's annual meeting, NewYork.

Southwick, S.M., Yehuda, R., Giller, E.L. (1991). Characterization of depression in war-related posttraumatic stress disorder. *American Journal of Psychiatry*, 148, 179–183.

Southwick, S.M., Yehuda, R., Giller, E.L. (1993). Personality disorders in treatment-seeking combat veterans with posttraumatic stress disorder. *American Journal of Psychiatry,*150:7, 1020–1023.

Speckhard, A. (1987). *Psycho-social stress following abortion.* Kansas City, MO: Sheed & Ward.

Spitzer, R.L., Williams, J.B.W., Gibbon, M. (1987). *Structured Clinical Interview for DSM-III-R* (patient version). New York: New York State Psychiatric Institute.

Water, W.W. (1980). Mental health consequences of abortion and refused abortion. *Canadian Journal of Psychiatry,* 25, 68–73.

Weisenberg, M., Solomon, Z., Schwarzwald, J., Mikulincer, M. (1987). Assessing the severity of posttraumatic stress disorder: Relation between dichotomous and continuous measures. *Journal of Consulting and Clinical Psychology,* 55, 432–434.

APPENDIX

Methodological Considerations in Empirical Research on Abortion

RACHEL L. ANDERSON, DAVID C. HANLEY,
DAVID B. LARSON, ROGER C. SIDER

INTRODUCTION

Research emphasis on the effects of elective abortion has changed over the last two decades, due in part to the development of new medical reproductive techniques, the changing roles of women in society, and public debate concerning the morality of abortion as a viable choice of pregnancy termination. Early research on the contextual nature of the abortion experience was focused on the woman's decision regarding her pregnancy (Speckhard, 1987). The outcome emphasis in this phase of research concentrated on adverse clinical effects, including psychiatric or medical complications of the abortion procedure (Adler, 1975; Cohen and Roth, 1984; Major, Mueller and Hildebrandt, 1985). More recently, research has begun to examine more fully the psychological sequelae and antecedents that affect a woman who seeks an abortion (Dagg, 1991).

In spite of growing literature on the psychological responses to abortion, numerous methodological difficulties face researchers attempting to understand the abortion experience. Reviews of the literature have documented several methodological flaws which hinder research development. Lyons et al. (1988) suggest that while studies have surveyed women from a period of hours after the abortion to ten years after their most recent abortion, most studies covered a year or less following the abortion experience. For example, measuring immediate post-abortion responses, Cohen and Roth (1984) investigated intrusion, avoidance, depression, and anxiety five hours post-abortion. Results indicate a significant improvement on these measures in women undergoing abortion procedures. Moseley et al. (1981) also found lower scores on measures of depression and anxiety when examining women prior to discharge after the abortion procedure. While prospective studies over the immediate course of the abortion provide some evidence that women feel relieved by the surgical abortion procedure, they do not provide adequate knowledge about the mental health impact of the abortion after a much longer period of time has elapsed. As it is a surgical procedure, it is expected that women undergoing abortion will have some anticipatory anxiety and distress regarding the safety of the procedure. These anticipatory emotions should remediate rapidly once the procedure has been completed. Thus, comparisons of emotional states immediately before and after the abortion should show relief and lowered distress. It would thus be some time later that psychological sequelae might likely manifest resulting from regret, guilt, or other thoughts and feelings concerning the abortion experience.

The timing of measurements as well as lack of substantial follow-up time periods are not the only conundrum for researchers. Doane and Quigley (1981) criticized the lack of adequate control groups, a prevalence of poorly defined and measured symptoms, and unspecified indications for the abortion. Studies examining mental health outcomes without comparison or control groups have tended to report a lack of significant negative responses in women. Cohen and Roth (1984) found lower scores on intrusion, avoidance, depression, and anxiety when measuring women five hours after the abortion procedure. Freeman et al. (1980) report that women undergoing their first abortion procedure had a significant reduction in scores on several scales including depression, anxiety, and an overall measure of emotional distress two weeks post-abortion. Major et al. (1985) assessed women immediately post-abortion and then three weeks later. Results indicate that over this brief time period women's scores improved on depression, mood, and anticipated consequences. Finally, Jacob et al. (1974) found significantly lower scores at one-month post-abortion on measures of depression, symptoms, and mood. In contrast, Robbins (1979) did not find significant differences between pre- and post-abortion periods. This study measured women at one-year post-abortion specifically concerning their regret and willingness to repeat the abortion procedure. However, as this and the above studies all lacked appropriate comparison conditions, it is not possible to extrapolate what effects are due to the abortion and what are due to historical and maturational processes that were neither measured nor controlled (Cook and Campbell, 1979).

Identifying a reasonable comparison group for women who undergo an elective abortion is complicated by the fact that so many factors are involved in this decision. It is not possible ethically to randomly assign women seeking an abortion to one of two conditions: abortion versus no abortion; thus, an absolute control group study is difficult to attain. Therefore, multiple approximations of such a control condition are needed. Some choices might be as follows:

Women who take their pregnancy to term

This group provides a comparison with women who do not seek an abortion. However, it is possible that they differ significantly from women seeking abortion on any number of psychological and socioeconomic variables. Also, those who chose parenting might have different outcomes than those who choose adoption.

Women who are denied abortion

This group appears an ideal comparison group *prima facie*; however, some notable differences may arise. It is likely that women who are denied abortions in circumstances where abortions are generally available might be different from women who chose to carry their pregnancy to term and as compared with women who received abortions. These differences must be better identified and understood. (Differences have been found between women who were denied abortion and women who experienced abortion procedures on outcomes of mental disturbance and emotional strain: Hook, 1963; Downer and Nash, 1978a, 1978b; Pare and Raven, 1970; for more research examining outcomes of denied abortion, see Dagg 1991.)

In addition to problems with the timing of measurement and the use of comparison samples, many studies suffer from significant problems with the definitions of outcomes studied. A recent review by Anderson et al. (1994) reports little use in the published peer-reviewed research of careful diagnostic criteria to specify the prevalence of psychiatric conditions that might be associated with or attributable to the experience of undergoing a previous elective abortion. Specifically, the deficiency of studies utilizing such diagnostic criteria does not allow for the estimation of the prevalence of depressive disorders or post-traumatic distress disorder. While a minority of studies use general measures of symptoms or mental health screens, such as a Symptom Checklist 90 or the Beck Depression Inventory, these instruments are only general measures of distress and cannot be used to reliably detect diagnosable conditions. Since few would posit that every woman who undergoes an abortion is subject to a negative psychological outcome, measures that result in comparison of means between groups may be inappropriate. Rather, research objectives need to be directed toward determining the level of risk for adverse psychological outcomes and what circumstances or predictors place women at increased risk for such adverse consequences.

Determining the prevalence of adverse psychological outcomes associated with abortion experiences and identifying risk factors predicting such outcomes requires careful sampling with measures assessing diagnostic outcomes, sufficient follow-up, and adequate comparison groups. Without appropriate comparisons it is not possible to understand any such estimates outside of the context of single, non-generalizable sample. The present chapter strives to provide a methodological framework and an illustrative study with which to approach the study of psychological consequences of abortion.

The published psychological effects of elective abortion are varied, ranging from positive, relieving effects to significant psychological distress and disorder. While this entire continuum merits examination, the focus of this chapter is on designing a research study to assess psychopathology and psychological distress. Ney et al. (1994) estimate that 25 per cent of women who have pregnancy losses feel they need professional help. These authors report that women who abort electively appear to require more frequent and more sophisticated grief counseling than those who suffer other types of pregnancy loss (e.g., stillbirth, miscarriage). Further, data reported by the American Psychological Association (1987) suggest that distress prevalence rates in the United States range from 0.5 per cent to 1.5 per cent. While most women who undergo abortions do not have negative psychological reactions, these data suggest that some women do experience negative psychological sequelae secondary to the abortion experience. These data indicate that rates of abortion-related distress occur with sufficient frequency to merit scientific investigation. Further, a detailed examination of the methodological issues facing researchers investigating negative psychological reaction will likely aid in future prevention and treatment efforts.

Part of the difficulty confronting those who wish to study the effects of pregnancy decisions is a failure to elaborate the variables that influence the course and outcome of this process. To this end, Figure 1 displays a theoretical model which represents a sequence of factors in order to focus methodological consideration for research on the psychological effects of abortion. A woman's route from pregnancy decision to post-abortion involves a multi-stage process of choices and influences both implicit and explicit, active and passive. Such influences include previous psychiatric difficulties, social support, and issues contributing to pregnancy decision.

INDIVIDUAL CHARACTERISTICS

Informing the understanding of how a woman decides on an abortion to terminate her pregnancy is a host of individual characteristics of that woman comprising her personality, history, and environment. Her beliefs and experiences inform her choice. The meaning of pregnancy and parenting also contributes. Speculating every potential contributing factor is of course impossible to elaborate and goes clearly beyond the focus of this chapter. However, since the present focus is on psychological outcomes, perhaps the most salient individual characteristic that must be considered is the woman's psychological wellbeing or adjustment prior to the pregnancy. The relatively low levels of both physical and psychological risk associated with elective abortion found in the literature (Anderson et al., 1994) suggest the factors apart from the procedure *per se* may be responsible for post-abortion distress. It appears that certain factors, such as previous psychiatric difficulties, put women at greater risk for poor psychological adjustment (Dagg, 1991). If prior psychological difficulties precurse negative or clinically harmful reactions to abortion, then it would be reasonable to propose that psychological processes play an important role in mediating women's response. This suggests that the process of coping with the abortion experience may vary across women dependent on the prior psychiatric difficulties. Prior psychiatric difficulties including treatment for a disorder may predict or be a risk factor for post-abortion emotional sequelae. Alternatively, those with grater psychological resources would be better able to cope with the experience.

PARTNER CHARACTERISTICS

One of the least studied aspects of the psychological effects of abortion is on the contribution of the male partner to the woman's post-abortion adjustment. It goes without saying that all pregnancies result from the actions of both a woman and a man. However, these actions can vary quite dramatically based on the nature of the relationship between the two people involved. For women in an ongoing relationship, the male's support for and participation in the decision to abort and the surgical procedure itself may play an important role (Ney et al., 1994). On the other hand, for women not in a relationship, the male's role may be quite different. A pregnancy which results from one of any number of partners is likely quite different than one that results from a monogamous relationship. In these situations, the male's participation may be less relevant or impossible. For a pregnancy that results from rape, the male's participation could be considered wholly negative for the woman. Thus, consideration of the nature of the woman's relationship to the impregnating male and that man's role in her pregnancy decision-making is a potentially important source of understanding the woman's eventual psychological adjustment to the elective abortion.

PREGNANCY DECISION LEADING TO ABORTION

In this phase of the sequence, many complex factors influence a woman's decision to abort or carry the fetus to term, including access, finances, health knowledge, values and attitudes. For example, concerning a woman's abortion decision-making, research indicates that a longer waiting period between conception and abortion may result in higher level of psychological stress on the woman. Research by Adler (1975) suggests that women who received first-trimester abortions experienced less difficulty with the decision to abort as compared to women who received mid-trimester abortions. This author also reported that women experiencing mid-trimester abortions were more likely to experience negative reactions post-abortion (see also Athanasiou et al., 1973).

Finally, factors surrounding the access, expense, and availability of abortion and adoption services are likely to influence decision-making. Cultural and lifestyle considerations also inform these decisions (Hanley et al., 1994).

ABORTION EXPERIENCE

Conceptual and theoretical models of response to abortion are helpful in guiding and structuring research initiatives. Such models aid researchers to adequately define predictors and outcomes and measure symptoms and diagnoses with objective standards allowing for reliable, replicable measurement and study. (However, caution warrants discarding all facts relevant to a particular theory once that theory comes under review and is discarded.

Some findings are dependable, others are not: Cook and Campbell, 1979.) Findings supported by replication of experimental results can be reinterpreted in an attempt to reframe new theories. At least three psychological models appear relevant to the consideration of women's psychological reactions to abortion: 1) post-traumatic stress disorder, 2) stress and coping, 3) existential/moral guilt.

The Post Traumatic Stress Disorder (PTSD) model assumes a diagnosable psychiatric disorder which results from a traumatic experience. In order to explain reactions to abortion within this model, DSM-IV criteria (Diagnostic Manual of the American Psychiatric Association, 4th edition) require that the experience of abortion be traumatic for the women and that the symptoms following the abortion be consistent with the symptom profile of PTSD and include persistent re-experiencing of the abortion, persistent avoidance of stimuli associated with the abortion, and persistent symptoms of increased arousal (DSM-IV, 1994).

The stress and coping model suggests that abortion is an event experienced at differing levels of stress to each woman and that a woman's coping style and resiliency would predict her response to the abortion experience. Insufficient ability to cope with an abortion experience is influenced by a complex interaction of various life factors including insufficient social support and psychosocial instability (Adler and Dolcini, 1986; Major et al., 1994), coercion by significant others to abort (Watters, 1980), and concomitant stress due to other major life events (Blumberg and Golbus, 1975; Moseley et al., 1981). Using this model, a woman would be at risk for adverse psychological outcome if she experienced the abortion as stressful and had poor coping abilities and limited social skills or available social support.

Finally, the existential/moral model suggests that healthy psychological adjustment to abortion would result if the woman were minimally morally conflicted or sufficiently morally comfortable with her decision and did not experience her choice as personally unacceptable in terms of her beliefs about the abortion. However, if the decision to abort conflicted with her moral beliefs and/or values, then the woman would be at risk for poor emotional adjustment to the extent she did not resolve her choice to abort in a manner consistent with her values and beliefs about abortion.

Figure 1: Theoretical Model of Pregnancy Decision-Making and Resolution

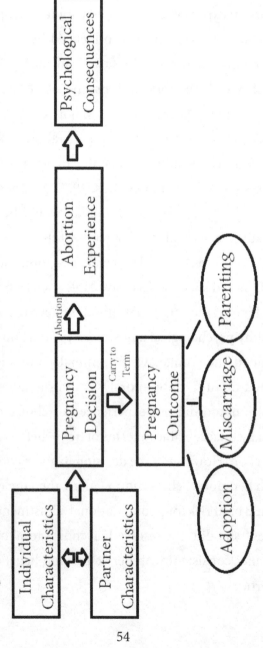

PINE REST STUDY

To address some of the methodological issues facing researchers examining mental health out- comes associated with abortion, we present the design of an American study of post-abortion stress conducted at Pine Rest Christian Hospital, located in Grand Rapids, Michigan. This study was designed to examine potential risk factors for long-term abor- tion-related distress in women. Specifically, this study tested whether or not women who reported distress from their experience fit a profile consistent with PTSD or an alternative model.

One treatment and two comparison groups were utilized. The two control groups helped to separate the effects attributable to the abortion from the effects attributable to irrelevancies that may have been associated with the abortion experience. Given the recognized risk for post-abortion in women with a history of psychiatric problems, three groups of women who were receiving outpatient psychiatric services were compared.

The treatment group was composed of a group of women who presented a positive history of elective abortion and sought psychiatric services in response to negative psychological adjustment to abortion. The first control group also presented with a positive history of elective abortion; however, reasons for seeking outpatient services were not abortion-related. The second control group sought outpatient services but denied any history of prior elective abortion. The average length of time across the experimental and first control groups between the abortion procedure and the research interviews was approximately nine years.

MEASURES

The selection of measures was guided by the principle of building on existing clinical and theoretical knowledge. Where possible, widely used measures with established reliability and validity were employed.

To assess PTSD symptomatology, the PTSD module of the Structured Clinical Interview for DSM-III-R (SCID-R; Spitzker, Williams and Gibbon, 1987), the MMPI-2 PK (Post-Traumatic Stress Disorder Scale) and PS (Post-Traumatic Stress Disorder Scale) scales (Keane, Malloy and Fairbank, 1984; Schlenger and Kulka, 1987, the Los Angeles

Symptom Checklist (LASC; Leskin and Foy, 1993), and the Impact of Event Scale (IES; Horowitz, Wilner and Alvarez, 1979) were utilized.

Employing several measures of PTSD symptomatology, each having different methods of recording responses, addressed primary threat to the construct validity of any measurement procedure as discussed by Cook and Campbell (1979). These authors report the importance of mono-method bias in experimental research stating that bias may occur when employing only one method of recording responses. The rationale is that the method is itself an irrelevancy (that no single method, e.g. self-report, is perfect) whose influence cannot be dissociated from the influence of target construct, in this case the assessment of PTSD symptomatology. Cook and Campbell suggest implementing several methods of measuring a construct to alleviate the concern of mono-method bias. We address this concern in the design of the Pine Rest study by utilizing four measures of PTSD symptomatology present in different forms; clinically structured interviews, semi-structured interview, and self-report measures.

Other measures used in the study that assessed stress and coping perspectives were the Interview for Recent Life Event (IRLE Paykel, 1974) which assessed the number and severity of stressful life events and the Social Support Questionnaire-6 (SSQ-6; Sarason, Sarason, Shearin and Pierce, 1987) which assessed the number of persons within one's social network perceived to be potential sources of social support, and one's satisfaction with the quality and extent of that social support.

Finally, the Abortion-Related Psychosocial History Interview (ARPHI; based in part of Speckhard's (1987) work) was designed for the study to gather information concerning the abortion experience including moral belief variables. While it is ill-advised to develop a measure specifically for a single study, the absence of relevant measures of abortion-relevant moral beliefs required the construction of this questionnaire.

RESULTS

The findings indicated a significantly higher rate of PTSD, as measured by the SCID-R, the LASC, and the Impact of Life Events Scale, among the abortion-distressed group as compared to women with a history of abortion who were seeking outpatient services for other problems. In fact, 73 per cent of women in the distressed group met the SCID-R criteria for PTSD. A significant difference was also found between the abortion-distressed women and the abortion-non-distressed women on a measure of moral belief. Women in the abortion-distressed group more often reported that they believed abortion to be morally wrong. There were no significant differences among groups on measures of psychopathology as measured in the MMPI-2, on overall social support, or religiosity. Further, abortion-distressed women experienced fewer recent adverse life events as compared to the abortion-non-distressed women.

Thus, the data suggest that some women experience PTSD as a result of elective abortion. It appears that this experience is not mediated by social support, other psychopathology or life events. It does appear that the occurrence of PTSD might be related to a woman's experience of the abortion as outside her normal values or morality.

DISCUSSION

The Pine Rest Study addressed several methodological considerations including the use of adequate control groups, reliable diagnostic criteria, and use of a theoretical model to direct research initiatives. The study also partially addressed the issue of adequate follow-up time periods. The finding that PTSD related to the abortion experience was present nearly a decade after the abortion demonstrates the importance of long-term follow-along studies. On the other hand, the study did not address when the PTSD developed over the time course. Future research should identify when at-risk women develop PTSD from abortion. Research that follows women for only a short time following the procedure may miss the development of PTSD altogether.

Additional limitations remain evident. The Pine Rest Study was a retrospective analysis evaluating psychiatric symptoms years after the abortion experience. Although such a design provides an important contribution to the overall understanding of post-abortion distress, such a design precludes determining whether the development of PTSD is related to the individual's emotional response at the times of the abortion. Prospective longitudinal studies that assess both the woman's experience of the abortion and her long-term adjustment are needed to better understand factors that may place some women at greater risk for PTSD. Longitudinal studies, however, can be time-consuming and expensive. Researchers need to consider the amount of time that will elapse between planning a longitudinal study and obtaining the results. It is likely that several years may pass between the conception of the experiment and the availability of results. When decisions have to be made quickly, such as policy decisions, researchers must weigh the advantages and disadvantages of different experimental designs that may best address timely concerns and be most suitable.

A second limitation is that the entire SCID was not given to participants; the SCID PTSD module was utilized alone. As Southwick et al. (1993) reports, high rates of comorbid psychopathology have been associated with PTSD including major depression and substance abuse. However, the presence of comorbid psychopathology not assessed in this study does not rule out the existence of PTSD. Future research should examine the effects of co-occurring disorders to better understand potentially more severe levels of diagnostic distress experienced by some women who have undergone previous abortion procedures. A more extensive understanding of PTSD and possible co-occurring disorders would provide clinicians with a more comprehensive understanding of women with abortion experiences seeking mental health services. Such understanding would aid in the development of more effective assessment, prevention, and treatment efforts for these women.

Third, the sample in the Pine Rest Study was gathered to specifically over-sample women who acknowledged that they had experienced difficulties in adjustment to their post-abortion experience. It is important to note that while the findings indicate that PTSD can result from a prior elective abortion, there is no evidence from the data on how frequently such a reaction might be observed. In an attempt to address such a concern, a longitudinal study of randomly selected women seeking abortion services could be conducted. From such a design, one would be able to assess the frequency of observed PTSD development.

Significant methodological difficulties face researchers attempting to better understand psychological reactions associated with the abortion experience. In this chapter, we have outlined a framework for better designs of research studies, thus improving research in this complicated area. It appears clear that not every woman who undergoes an abortion has psychological difficulties. On the other hand, significant psychiatric problems can result from this experience. With careful selection of measures, assessment points, and comparison groups, an understanding of which women are at-risk for the development of adverse psychological sequelae of abortion can be achieved.

REFERENCES

N.E. Adler (1975), 'Emotional responses of women following therapeutic abortion', *American Journal of Orthopsychiatry*, 45, 446-54.

N.E. Adler and P. Dolcini (1986), 'Psychological issues in abortion for adolescents' in G.B. Melton (ed.), *Adolescent abortion: psychological and legal issues* (University of Nebraska Press, Lincoln, Nebraska).

American Psychiatric Association, *Diagnostic and Statistical Manual of Mental Disorders*, 4th ed. (American Psychiatric Association Press, Washington, DC).

American Psychological Association (1987), 'The psychological sequelae of abortion', Research review presented to the Office of the Surgeon General of the United States of America on behalf of the Public Interest Directorate of the American Psychological Association.

R. L. Anderson, J.S. Lyons and D.B. Larson (1994) 'A systematic review of the physical, psychological and social impact of elective abortion on women. Paper presented to the American Psychological Association's conference on Psychosocial and Behavioral Factors in Women's Health: Creating an agenda for the 21st century' (Washington, DC, May).

R. Athanasiou, W.C. Oppel and L. Michelson, et al. (1973), 'Psychiatric sequelae to term birth and induced early and late abortion: a longitudinal study', *Family Planning Perspectives*, 5, 227–31.

B.D. Blumberg, M.S .Golbust and K.H. Hanson (1975), 'The psychological sequelae of abortion performed for a genetic indication', *American*

Journal of Obstetrics and Gynecology, 122, 799–808.

T. Cohen and S. Roth (1984), 'Coping with abortion', *Journal of Human Stress*, 10, 140–5.

T. Cook and D.T. Campbell (1979), *Quasi-experimentation. Design and analysis issues for field setting* (New York: Houghton Mifflin).

P.K.B. Dagg (1991), 'The psychological sequelae of therapeutic abortion—denied and completed', *American Journal of Psychiatry*, 148, 578–85.

B.K. Doane and B.G. Quigley (1981), 'Psychiatric aspects of therapeutic abortion', *Canadian Medical Association*, 125, 427–32.

S.J. Drower and E.S. Nash (1978a), 'Therapeutic abortion on psychiatric grounds, part I: A local study', *South African Journal of Medicine*, 54, 604–8.

S.J. Drower and E.S. Nash (1978b), 'Therapeutic abortion on psychiatric grounds, part II: The continuing debate', *South African Journal of Medicine*, 54, 643–7.

E.W. Freeman and K. Rickels, G.R. Huggins, C. R. Garcia and J. Polin (1980), 'Emotional distress patterns among women having first or repeat abortions', *Obstetrics and Gynecology*, 55, 630–6.

D.C. Hanley, R. L. Anderson, D.B. Larson and R.C. Sider (1994), 'Post-traumatic abortion related stress in psychiatric outpatients: Comparisons among abortion-distressed, abortion-non-distressed, and no abortion group' submitted for publication.

K. Hook (1963), 'Refused abortion. A follow-up study of 249 women whose applications were refused by the National Board of Health in Sweden', *Acta Psychiatrica Scandinavia*, 168, 3–153 (Suppl).

M. Horowitz, H. Wilner and W. Alvarez (1979), 'Impact of Events Scale: A measure of subjective stress', *Psychosomatic Medicine*, 41, 209–18.

D. Jacobs, C.R. Garcia, K. Rickels and R.W. Preucel (1974), 'A prospective study on the psychological effects of therapeutic abortion', *Comprehensive Psychiatry*, 15, 423–34.

T.M. Keane, P.F. Malloy and J.A. Fairbank (1984), 'Empirical development of an MMPI subscale for the assessment of combat-related post-traumatic stress disorder', *Journal of Consulting and Clinical Psychology*, 52, 888–91.

G. Leskin and D. Foy (1993), 'The Los Angeles Symptom Checklist. Paper presented at the 9th annual meeting of the International Society for Traumatic Stress Studies' (San Antonio, TX).

J.S. Lyons, D.B. Larson, W.M. Huckeba, J.L. Rogers and C.P. Mueller (1988), 'Research on the psychosocial impact of abortion: A systematic review of the literature 1966 to 1985', in G. P. Reiger (ed.), *Values and Public Policy, Family Research Council* (Washington, DC).

B. Major, J.M. Zubek, L. Cooper and C. Cozzarelli (1994), 'Social conflict, social support, and adjustment to abortion. Paper presented to the American Psychological Association's conference on Psychosocial and Behavioral Factors in Women's Health: Creating an agenda for the 21st century' (Washington, DC, May).

B. Major, P. Mueller and K. Hildebrandt (1985), 'Attributions, expectations, and coping with abortion', *Journal of Personality and Social Psychology*, 48, 585–99.

O.T. Moseley, D.R. Follingstad, H. Harley and R. Heckel (1981), 'Psychological factors that predict reaction to abortion', *Journal of Clinical Psychology*, 37, 276–9.

P.G. Ney, T. Fung, A.R. Wickett and C. Beamon-Dodd (1994), 'The effects of pregnancy loss on women's health', *Social Science Medicine*, 38, 1193–1200.

C.M.B. Pare and H. Raven (1970), 'Psychiatric sequelae to therapeutic abortion: Follow-up of patients referred for termination of pregnancy', *Lancet*, I, 635–8.

E.S. Paykel (1974), 'Life stress and psychiatric disorder: Application of the clinical approach' in B.P. Dohrenwend and B.S. Dohrenwend (eds.). *Stressful life events: Their nature and effects*, pp. 135–49. (New York: Wiley).

J.M. Robbins (1979), 'Objective versus subjective responses to abortion', *Journal of Consulting and Clinical Psychology, 47, 994–5.*

I.G. Sarason, B.R. Sarason, E.N. Shearin and G.R. Pierce (1987), "A brief measure of social support: Practical and theoretical limitations', *Journal of Social and Personal Relationships*, 4, 497–510.

W.E. Schlenger and R.A. Kulka (1987), 'Performance of Keane-Fairbank MMPI Scale and other self-report measures in identifying post-traumatic stress disorder'. Paper presented at the American Psychological Association annual meeting (New York).

S.M. Southwick, R. Yehuda and E. L. Giller (1993), 'Personality disorders in treatment-seeking combat veterans with post-traumatic stress disorder', *American Journal of Psychiatry*, 150, 1020–3.

A. Speckhard (1987), *Psychosocial stress following abortion* (Sheed & Ward, Kansas City, Missouri).

R.L. Spitzer, J.B.W. Williams and M. Gibbon (1987) *Structured Clinical Interview for DSM-III-R* (patient version). New York: New York State Psychiatric Institute.

W.W. Waters (1980), 'Mental health consequences of abortion and refused abortion', *Canadian Journal of Psychiatry*, 25, 68–73.

ABOUT THE AUTHORS

At the time of the writing in 1995:

David C. Hanley, MSW, was a Senior Clinical Social Worker at Pine Rest Christian Hospital in Grand Rapids, Michigan. Trained at the University of Michigan School of Social Work, he has specialized in treatment of women stressed by their abortions and has served as principal investigator of a clinical research study of post-abortion stress conducted at Pine Rest Christian Hospital.

Rachel L. Anderson was a doctoral student in the Human Development and Social Policy Program at Northwestern University, Evanston, Illinois. Her research focus was on women's health, including completion of a systematic review of the medical, psychological and social effects of induced abortion on women, funded by the U.S. Department of Health and Human Services.

David B. Larson, MD, MSPH, was Adjunct Professor of Psychiatry at Duke University Medical Center, Northwestern University Medical School and the United States Uniformed Health Services. A former research psychiatrist at the National Institute of Mental Health and the U.S. Department of Health and Human Services, he then became President of the National Institute of Healthcare Research. Dr. Larson helped to develop the systematic review methodology and specialized in the public policy implication of religious commitment. He had over 160 professional publications in such policy areas as mental health diagnoses and services, the use of nursing homes, and AIDS/HIV infection.

Harry L. Piersma worked most of his career at Pine Rest Christian Hospital in Grand Rapids, Michigan, and later retired from the W.G. Hefner VA Medical Center in Salisbury, North Carolina.

D. Stephen King, MD, was a Staff Psychiatrist Pine Rest Christian Hospital in Grand Rapids, Michigan.

Roger C. Sider, MD, was a Medical Director of the Pine Rest Christian Hospital in Grand Rapids, Michigan, and professor of Human Medicine at Michigan State University. Trained at the University of Toronto and Johns Hopkins Hospital, he has published numerous articles and book chapters on psychiatric ethics and had a life-long interest in clinical care, clinical administration, and the interface of psychiatry and religion.